WHO RANG THE CHURCH BELL?

Written by Edward Hujsak
Illustrated by Willis Goldsmith

Published by
Mina-Helwig Company
La Jolla, California

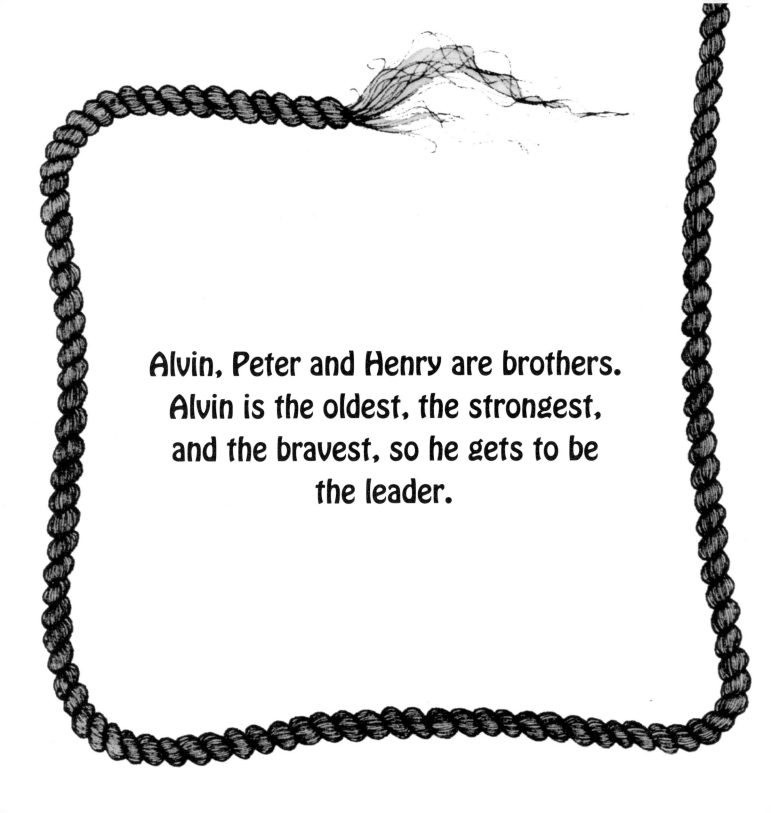

Alvin, Peter and Henry are brothers.
Alvin is the oldest, the strongest,
and the bravest, so he gets to be
the leader.

Alvin, Peter and Henry are church mice.
They live in a little white church that
has a big front door and stone steps.
The church has a steeple and a belfry
on top with a bell in it. The preacher
rings the bell every Sunday to call
all the people to church.

Alvin, Peter and Henry live in the belfry.
They can look out over the whole village
and see everything that is happening.

The church bell rings when the preacher pulls on a long rope that is tied to it.

When the bell rings it is very loud
in the belfry. Alvin, Peter and Henry
have to hold their ears.

Alvin, Peter and Henry always have plenty to eat. On Monday, the day after church service, they run up and down the pews and aisles, collecting communion crumbs. That always gives them enough food to nibble until Thursday.

On Thursday night the choir comes to the church to practice their singing. Afterwards the people always have punch and cookies for a snack. When they munch their cookies, some cookie crumbs fall to the floor.

After the choir leaves the church.
Alvin, Peter and Henry scurry into
the practice room and collect all
the cookie crumbs. That way
they always have enough to eat
until Sunday.

Alvin, Peter and Henry always
attend the church services. They peek
out from above the roof beams where
no one can see them. They like the
singing the best.

One Sunday the preacher was very angry. He shouted, "Where is everyone? This church is too empty! We cannot go on this way! After today, this church will be closed!" That Sunday the people filed sadly out of the church.

The preacher closed the door behind them.
Thunk! Then he turned a big
key in the door lock so no one
could enter the church.

Alvin, Peter and Henry sat in the belfry to talk about the problem. "What, oh what will we do?" Peter said. Henry said, "We will starve to death with no crumbs to eat." "Let me think," Alvin said. Then he said, "I have an idea. If we can get the people to come to the church again, then everything will be o.k."

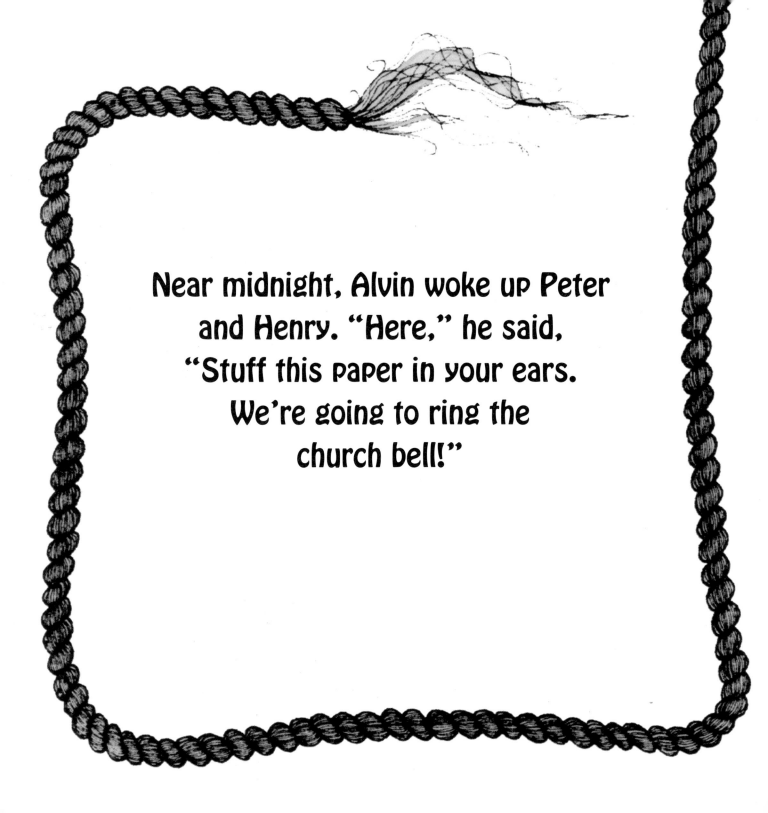

Near midnight, Alvin woke up Peter
and Henry. "Here," he said,
"Stuff this paper in your ears.
We're going to ring the
church bell!"

Alvin, Peter and Henry pulled and
pulled on the church bell rope,
and the church bell rang and rang
and rang.

The villagers woke up and looked out of their windows. Who could be ringing the church bell? The next day no one could discover why the church bell rang. The next midnight and the next, Alvin Peter and Henry rang the church bell again and again.

The butcher said to the house wife,
"Its a sign!"

The postman said to the florist,
"Its a sign!"

The farmer said to the beekeeper,
"Its a sign!"

The next Sunday a crowd gathered in front of the church. Some people were banging on the church door. "Open the door!" they shouted. "We want to come in!"

The preacher came and unlocked the
door and threw it open, and the
people filled the church. Alvin, Peter
and Henry looked happily down
from their perch, hidden away, high up on
the roof beams.

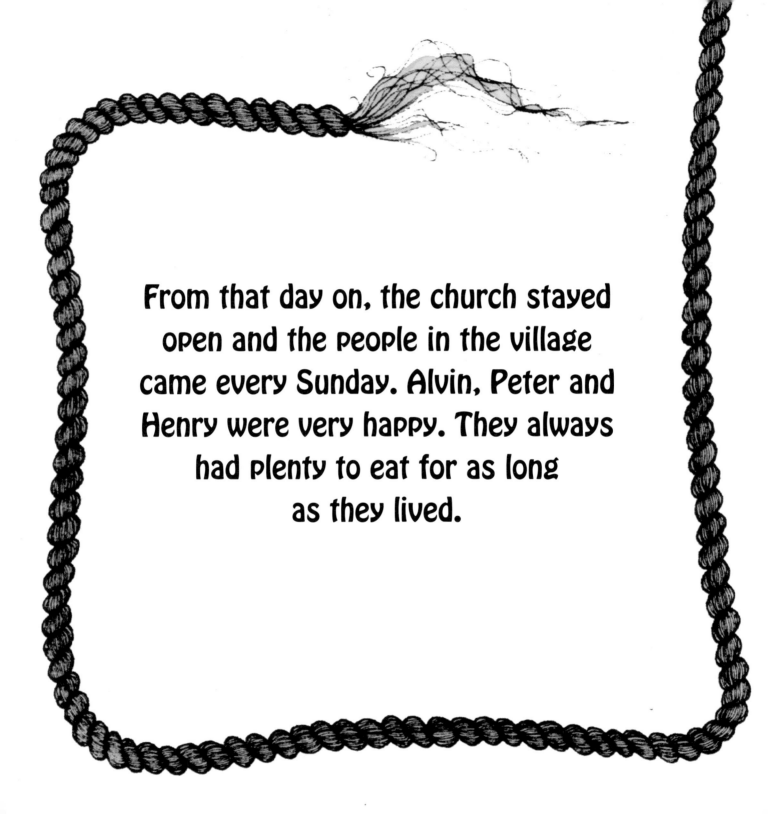

From that day on, the church stayed
open and the people in the village
came every Sunday. Alvin, Peter and
Henry were very happy. They always
had plenty to eat for as long
as they lived.